Couches Eat Shoes

AVA RATERMANN

J. Kenkade
PUBLISHING

Bryant, Arkansas

J. Kenkade Publishing
5920 Highway 5 N Ste. 7
Bryant, AR 72022
www.jkenkadepublishing.com
Facebook.com/jkenkadepublishing

J. Kenkade Publishing is a registered trademark.
Printed in the United States of America
ISBN: 978-1-955186-48-3

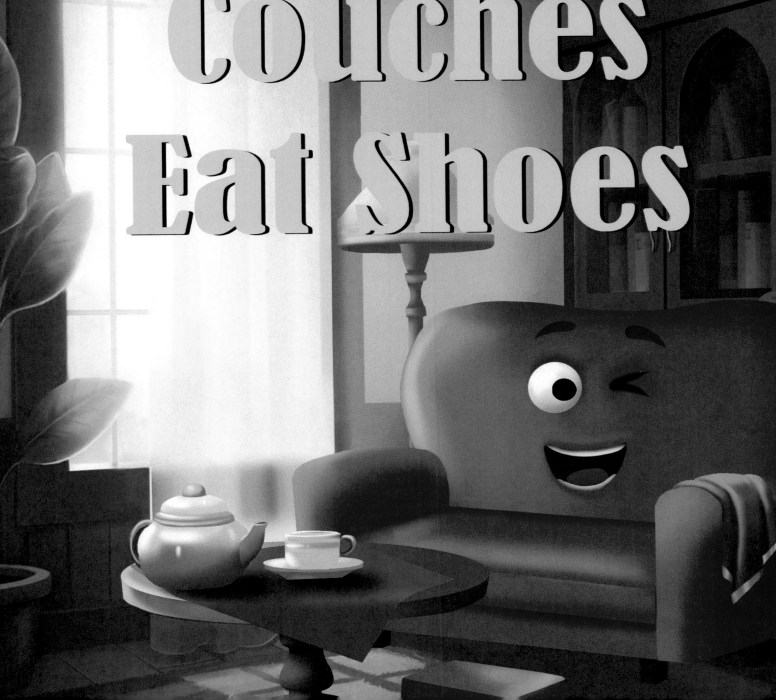

Couches look friendly
All cozy and warm
But don't let than fool you
They can do harm.

Couches have eyeballs
They watch while you sleep
They want something you have
On each of your feet.

Couches move quiet
You don't know what you'll lose
And while you're not looking
Couches eat shoes!

So, now that you're wiser
And know the whole truth
Keep your feet off the sofa
'Cause couches eat shoes!

About the Author

Ava Ratermann

My name is Ava Ratermann. I am 10 years old. I love to read books and write stories. To me, reading takes you to imaginary places. In writing stories, I can create my own world and make it as magical as I want. I hope my book offers you a way to escape into that world of wonder and fantasy. Happy Reading!

Enjoyed this Book?

Check out this children's book by
J. Kenkade Publishing

Enjoyed this Book?

Check out this children's book by
J. Kenkade Publishing

Enjoyed this Book?

Check out this children's book by J. Kenkade Publishing

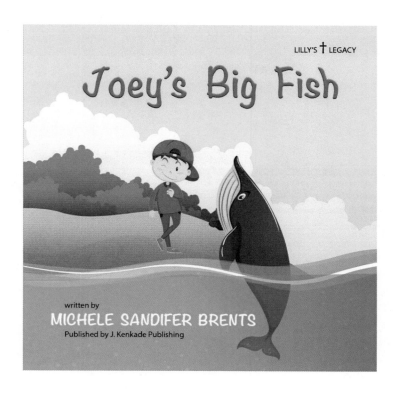

Enjoyed this Book?

Check out this children's book by
J. Kenkade Publishing

Made in the USA
Columbia, SC
19 July 2023

20645110R00015